Killer Puzzles

ATTACK OF THE KILLER PUZZLES

Kjartan Poskitt

Illustrated by Chris Fisher

SCHOLASTIC INC.

New York Toronto London Auckland Sydney
Mexico City New Delhi Hong Kong

ISBN 0-439-15525-8

12 11 10 9 8 7 6 5 4 3 2 1   0 1 2 3 4 5/0

Printed in the U.S.A.   40

First Scholastic printing, January 2000

They're here!

All across the nation, knees are knocking and brains are boiling. And it's all because of

THE ATTACK of the "KILLER PUZZLES"

They're so awful and horrible that they might even make you break out in a rash. They could even be FATAL, but nobody has survived long enough to tell us.

So are you brave, brash, and brainy enough to take them on? It's worth it, because if you battle your way through all of them, you'll be able to decode the DEADLY SECRET MESSAGE at the end. That's when the fun really starts!

Then you can pass this book on to someone else, and that person CANNOT POSSIBLY SURVIVE! Not even your teacher or the brainiest person on TV or even the PRESIDENT. In fact, you'll be able to pass this book on to ANYONE, and they will suffer ETERNAL GRUESOME MISERY from the Killer Puzzles. Ha-ha!

WARNING: If you only get one answer wrong, this book will make you SCREAM!

There are THREE THINGS to remember as you try to defeat the Killer Puzzles:

THING NUMBER ONE: Every puzzle will tell you where to go next. YOU MUST DO THE PUZZLES IN THE ORDER YOU ARE TOLD. For instance, your first puzzle is the Eyesore Jigsaw on page 6, and when you've solved it you will be told which page to go to. If you go to some other page you might find yourself doing the same puzzles over and over again.

THING NUMBER TWO: DANGER MESSAGES! If you reach a page with a danger message on it, you MUST do what it says. (If somebody else is doing these puzzles, look over their shoulder and make sure they follow the instructions – and have a good laugh!)

THING NUMBER THREE: CODE LETTERS. Most pages have one or more code letters in a little box at the top. Now, have a quick look at THE VERY BACK PAGE. Have you looked at it? Good.

Every time you reach a page with code letters at the top, you must enter them into the boxes on THE BACK PAGE in the right order. You'll see that there are a couple of code letters above the first puzzle on page 6, and these have already been filled in on THE BACK PAGE to start you off. Your next letter will go in box number 3, your next in box number 4, and so on. This is the most vitally important thing in the whole book! If you forget even one measly code letter, you will never get the DEADLY SECRET MESSAGE! And of course, the deadly secret message reveals just how foul, dastardly, and fiendish the Killer Puzzles really are.

There are some hints scattered through the book, but if all else fails you are advised to SCREAM. (After all, these are *Killer* Puzzles.)

OK, you're on your own. Take a deep breath, turn the page, and GOOD LUCK!

The Eyesore Jigsaw

Here's a picture of some skyscrapers made up of 25 square tiles.

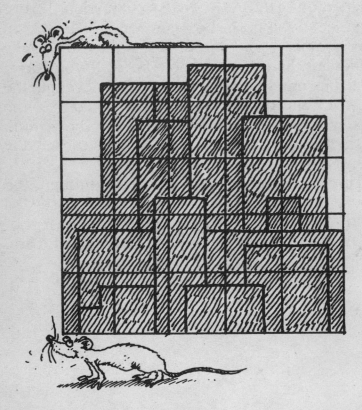

The tiles can be moved around to make a different pattern, but this pattern leaves out one of the tiles.

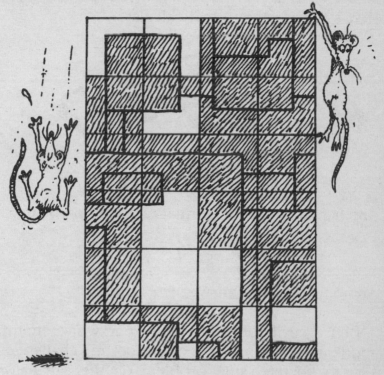

Can you see which of these five tiles is the missing one? Turn to the page number shown by the tile.

52   70   60   68   86

The Killer Calculator

Here's a perfectly normal calculator:

And here's a perfectly normal calculator problem:

$$9\ 0\ 1 + 2 - 6\ 1 + 5 =$$

And of course, the answer is 847.

BUT ... evil rules, because your worst enemy suddenly jumps out of an old teapot and challenges you to do the same problem on the calculator WITH YOUR EYES CLOSED. In other words, you have to remember the positions of the keys and press them in the right order. "Easy as pie," you say, and you close your eyes.

Unfortunately, your worst enemy has moved the keys on your calculator around without you knowing. You press what you think are the right keys, but the problem comes out completely different!

Look at how the keys have been reorganized. The first keys you push will be:

$$1\ 5\ -\ \_\ \_\ \_\ \_\ \_\ \_\ \_\ =$$

Can you fill in the rest of the new problem and work out the new answer? Turn to that page.

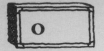

The Three-Sided Pegs

Here's a nice little baby game for you: fit the pegs in the holes. In fact, to make it even easier, all the pegs and the holes are the same shape. There's just one tiny detail: you must make all three arrows point toward the same number, because that's your next page.

(11)

(54)

(86)

(31)

(68)

(52)

(50)

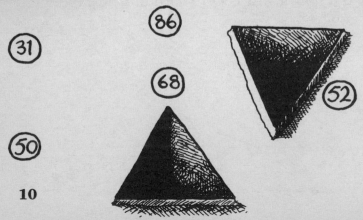

The Easy Page

Some people find the Killer Puzzles too hard, so this is the EASY PAGE. It's in nice big letters so it's easy to read.

In fact, this page is SO easy that, just to make it interesting, before you start you must go and put a teaspoon in the refrigerator.

Which was the last page you were on? (Look at the bottom of the LEFT-HAND page.) Spell the number out in big letters. Ready?

Now cross off the last three letters. What's left? Well, that's the page you go to next.

There, that was easy, wasn't it? Or maybe it wasn't . . . maybe when you crossed off the last three letters you didn't get a number? Uh-oh! In that case you'd better go back to the refrigerator, get the teaspoon out, and DROP IT DOWN THE BACK OF YOUR NECK!

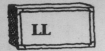

The Unfair Funfair

Here we are at the Unfair Funfair, and this is the bowling alley. You can knock over as many different pins as you like, then add up the points and see which prize you've won.

These are the numbers on the pins:

Here are the prizes and the points you need to win them:

CUDDLY PORCUPINE
14 POINTS

OLD SOCK PERFUME
11 POINTS

12

Antique Fish and french fries
16 POINTS

FLUFF COLLECTION
22 POINTS

SOGGY TOILET-PAPER ROLL
24 POINTS

CHEESE-AND-ONION-FLAVOR CHOCOLATES
28 POINTS

RUBBER SCREWDRIVER
30 POINTS

Can you see why it's so unfair? Yes, there is one prize that you can't possibly win. Work out which score is impossible to get, then turn to that page number.

The Page You've Been Waiting For!

Have you been through the book? Have you completed the code grid on the very last page? Did it make sense? If so,

YOU'VE DONE IT!
You've beaten the Killer Puzzles!

Award yourself three hours of your favorite TV program, eating your favorite food, wearing your favorite clothes, and sitting in your favorite chair. Bend your mouth round sideways and give yourself a big kiss on the cheek, then shake your own hand.

Now here comes the *really* fun part. (But it's only fun if you really have managed to decode the message on the last page. If you haven't, then you'd better go back and work it out.) Pass this book to somebody else, and watch them try to do the Killer Puzzles! When they go wrong, or when they need hints, make sure they do ALL the penalties!

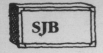

You've done something wrong! Yes, you have, and so you must be punished. Draw a picture of your own head on the opposite page:

Ha-ha! You are now trapped by the . . .

Chains of Doom!

On the floor of the dungeon is a set of heavy iron balls, and you are chained to some of them.

Can you see which numbers you are attached to and add them up? That will tell you which page to go to next.

By the way, if you don't get the answer right, you will never be released. The man next to you was told that, too, and look what happened to him!

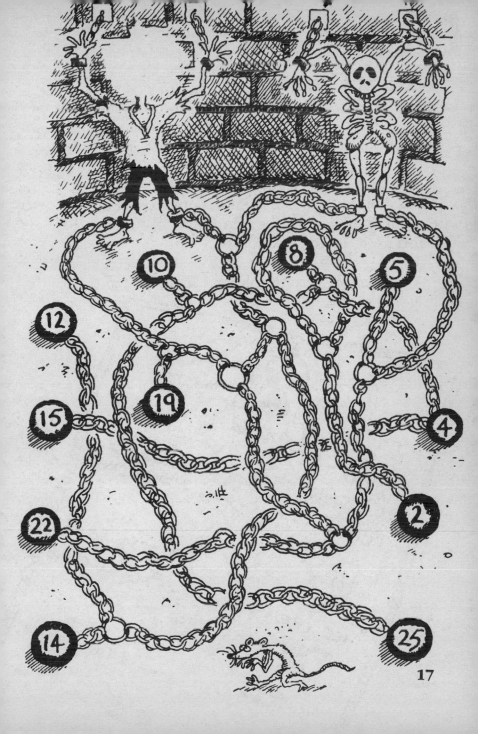

17

Killer Curry

Good grief, we've suddenly arrived in the mysterious East, at the Restaurant of a Thousand Tips, which is noted for its Killer Curry. One mouthful makes steam come out of your nose. Two mouthfuls make steam come out of your ears. If you have three mouthfuls, you have to stand up to let the steam out.

The menu is very simple and includes the price in gold coins.

The curry is so hot that for each plateful you'll have to eat at least one and a half bowls of ice cream. BUT . . . the ice cream is pretty awful, so you'll need three drinks for each full bowl you eat. (And you can't order half portions of anything.)

OK, here's your **KILLER CHALLENGE:**

If you have 50 gold coins, what's the biggest number of curries you can eat?

If you can only manage **ONE**, turn to page 88.

If you can manage **TWO**, turn to page 34.

If you can manage **THREE**, turn to page 11.

If you can manage **FOUR**, turn to page 83.

The Knight's Challenge

Here is a knight from a game of chess. They have a strange way of moving around the board: they jump in L-shaped moves.

To work out where the knight can land, you move two squares in any direction (not diagonally) and then one step to the side. This diagram shows a knight making four moves. Can you see how all his jumps are L-shaped? You'll notice that he always lands on a square of a different color from the one he starts on.

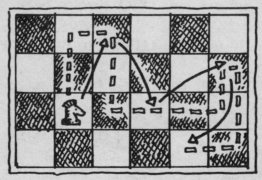

Now look at this special chess board. The knight is NOT allowed to land on any squares that are cracked (but he can jump over them). However, he should be able to move around and land on all the numbers except one. You have to find the only number he can't reach, because that's your next page number.

You're just in time to help the great detective Sheerluck Holmes solve the mystery of the stolen diamonds.

Of the five nasty villains in front of you, you know that two of them were involved. One was the burglar, and one was the getaway driver. Each of them has made a statement.

> Fingers is definitely one of the two crooks you want!
>
> BLAGSY 8

> I can drive, but I didn't have anything to do with it, and neither did Nobby.
>
> FINGERS 18

In fact, you know that only TWO of the villains tell the truth all the time, the others lie all the time. The trouble is, you don't know which is which. But can you work out which two were involved?

Add up both their numbers and turn to that page.

The Nasty Candy!

Yum, what a fabulous box of chocolates! Some of them have already been eaten, but most of them are still left. The trouble is that one of them is the PIGGY DRIBBLE SURPRISE.

Gertie Glutt has already eaten the candy that was two down from the orange cream. The strawberry whirl is three along from the orange cream. The peppermint squidge is three down from the one Mr. Snuffle had, and the caramel delight is two up from the one Mrs. Guzzle had. The praline mystery is two to the right of the caramel delight.

The piggy dribble surprise is not next to the peppermint squidge, but it is in between the toffee truffle and the coffee chomp. Can you see which number it is? Turn to that page.

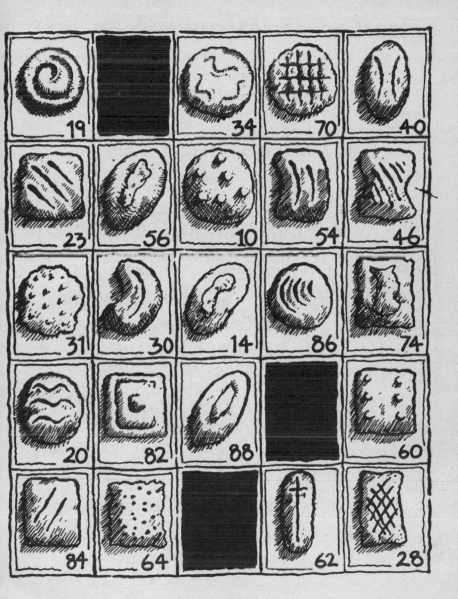

19

34 70 40

23 56 10 54 46

31 30 14 86 74

20 82 88 60

84 64 62 28

The Deadly Diner

Quick, tie a knot in your tongue and block your mouth up, because for your next Killer Puzzle you have to come to Sam and Ella's diner, which is the smelliest café in the universe.

Sam and Ella have two menus. This is the cheap one:

SAM 'n ELLA'S

* SQUELCHY CHEESE
* EGG YOGURT
* LIVER PUDDING
* UNSLICED BREAD
* ONION DELIGHT

Yummy! But while you choose what to have, there's a game to play. By circling one letter in each item and then reading down, you'll find you can spell out a number. Can you see it? Here's a clue: the answer is SEVEN. (Gosh, that was a very big clue.)

Here's the fancy menu:

SAM and ELLA'S

- FISH TAILS
- SNAKE PIE
- CHICKEN A LA DIRT
- YELLOW SAUSAGES
- SOGGY FRENCH FRIES
- TOAST ON TOAST
- OSTRICH JELLY
- BEEF SAUCE
- FLAT COLA
- MOLDY MILK SHAKES
- ORANGE PIP JUICE
- MUSHROOM ICE CREAM

By circling one letter from each item and reading down, can you find the hidden number?

Oh, by the way, there are two extra items on the menu that shouldn't be there, so you won't need them to spell out the number.

WARNING: The smell is getting worse . . . hold your breath until you're told it's safe to breathe again!

The Abandoned Mine

Now for some earthshaking fun, as we go underground to the dark, dangerous, abandoned mine.

Scattered around the mine are lots of treasures. The trouble is, there are some big rocks blocking the path. Luckily, there are also some sticks of dynamite to help you clear the rocks away. (It takes one whole stick of dynamite to explode one rock.)

If you plan your path correctly you'll find you can pick up extra dynamite as you go along. You should be able to collect ALL the treasures except one.

You have to find the number of the one treasure you can't collect, and go to that page.

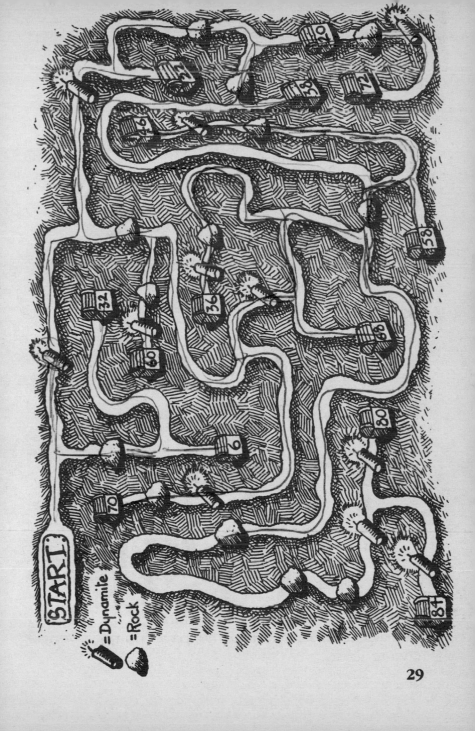

29

Before you go on, are you holding an item of clothing tightly in your hand?

NO? Then you can start the puzzle right away.

YES? Then you must pull the item over your mega-brainy head, lean out of the window, and sing "Gloopy gloopy gloo" at the first person to walk past. If that hasn't dented your confidence, then it's time to shape up to . . .

The Shapes

You'll see that you can use these three shapes to make various numbers, including

47, 14, 61, 74, 71

Can you find one more number the three shapes can make? That's the page number you have to go to.

Warning! System Error!

The computer that printed out the Killer Puzzles had a bit of a system failure, and you might have been misdirected. Are you sure you're supposed to be here? There's one way to check. What was the last letter you entered into a box on the back page? If it was W, then use the EMERGENCY PROCEDURE.

If it was O, X, J, P, B, or S, then check the last puzzle you did very carefully. Does it seem OK? Maybe you should check the one you did before that. And the one before that. In fact, check them all. Do they seem right? In that case you'd better check you've got the right book. Maybe you should go right back to where you bought the book and check the shop, too.

If it was any other letter, then go and put on every sock you can find and wear ALL of them ALL day.

EMERGENCY PROCEDURE: Check what page number you've just come from. (Look at the bottom of the LEFT-HAND page.) Write down the number backward (so if it was page 98, write down 89). Now multiply this number by two. What's the answer? Go to that page, but please remember, the KILLER PUZZLES INTERNATIONAL CORPORATION cannot be held responsible for the consequences. Good luck.

The Phantom Photographs

Yikes! This camera takes pictures all by itself.

Just the other day it was left on the table. There was nobody else in the room, but it managed to take six photographs. Can you work out what order it took them in?

There's just one problem . . . one photograph is a spooky extra photograph! It doesn't fit the sequence, and so it cannot possibly have been taken!

Can you work out which number is the Phantom Photo?

Gotcha!

Ha-ha . . . the Killer Puzzles were obviously too much for you. However, you've done well to get this far, so providing you pay a small penalty you'll get some helpful advice.

All you've got to do is lick your nose. Done it? OK, now you can have some help.

If you just came from the RESTAURANT OF A THOUSAND TIPS, you probably thought you were one measly gold coin short of being able to eat three curries. The thing is, to eat three curries you need to eat four and a half ice creams. Yes, yes, I know you have to buy five ice creams, but if you only eat four and a half of them, how many drinks will you need? Go back and try again.

If you were trying to find the PIGGY DRIBBLE SURPRISE, then the chocolate you picked to get here was the coffee chomp.

If you have had trouble in OUTER SPACE, here's a clue: do NOT use the warp beam between stations 46 and 34.

So you thought the cheapest clown outfit was $35, eh? Quite frankly, there's only one possible penalty for going wrong on the clown puzzle. That's right! You know that glass of water you've got sitting next to you? I'm afraid you have to pour it into your pants. HA-HA-HA!

Now then, Drippy Pants (you don't mind if I call you that, do you?), I'll give you a hint. When you buy the VERY cheapest clown outfit, you'll find that you actually have spares of some of the items, and you don't need to spend more than $10 on any one box. You'd better try again, shouldn't you? (And don't forget to fill that glass of water up again before you do.)

Maybe you thought horse 35 won the DOUBTFUL DERBY? Well, actually, it came in third, so there.

The Smelly Pyramid

Here are some cute little building bricks, all pyramid-shaped . . . except that one of them is not a brick, it's a STINK BOMB! If you so much as touch it, it will release the aroma of a thousand sweaty camels.

All the bricks are exactly the same, but the bomb is slightly different. Can you tell which one it is?

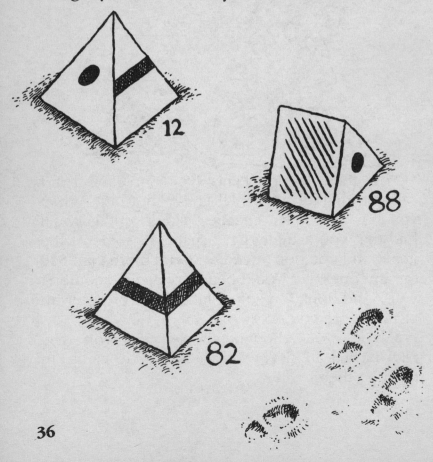

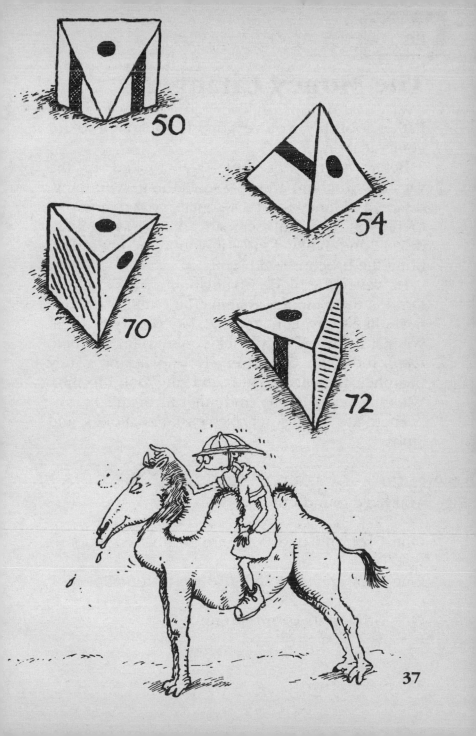

50

54

70

72

The Money Changer

Rather foolishly, you've gone to Outer Orrid for your vacation.

Before you went there you looked in the vacation brochure and saw sunbathing, swimming, discos, and fancy food. Of course, now that you're there you can still see sunbathing, swimming, discos, and fancy food – if you remembered to bring the brochure with you.

However, the biggest pain about going to Outer Orrid is their money system. The Outer Orridians never like to explain it so that they can try to cheat you. Of course, if they think you're trying to cheat *them*, they can be extremely unpleasant. (They pick their toenails in cafés and sing along to their Walkmans on the bus, and other nice stuff.)

There are three sorts of coins: Grots, Pokes, and Stubs.

You have found out that:

One Grot and one Poke are worth two Stubs.

One Grot and one Stub are worth four Pokes.

One Grot on its own is worth $10.

Happily, your vacation has come to an end, and in your pocket you have one Stub and three Pokes.

To avoid being cheated, can you work out how many Grots this is worth? (It's an exact number.) When you've done that, you'll know how many dollars to expect back from the money changer – which is also the number of your next page!

Welcome To Outer Orrid.

The Ghastly Guest House

Oh dear. . . here's the most perilous puzzle yet! You've got to stay a night at the Ghastly Guest House, which is uncomfortably close to Ghastly Castle.

Have you ever been to Ghastly Castle? It's haunted by a fiendish phantom, so I expect you're too scared. Mind you, if you're VERY brave, you could see the phantom in another brilliant Killer Puzzles book called *Find the Phantom of Ghastly Castle*.

The Ghastly Guest House has sixteen guest rooms laid out as shown on page 43. There's a door in every wall to connect each room with the ones next to it.

Sir Gustave Ghastly has shown you to room 52. You brush your hair, shoes and teeth and go to bed (wishing you had more than one brush).

CRASH! You hear a terrible sound! It seems that the six-tonne chandelier over in room 139 has collapsed.

The noise has shaken you up, so you decide to try and settle your nerves by moving all your stuff through the door into one of the rooms next to the one you are in, and go to bed there. (In other words, from room 52 you can go to room 28, 38 or 12.)

HISS! A nest of poisonous cobras suddenly comes alive in room 70. To take your mind off it, you decide to move again to one of the rooms next to the one

you are in. (You might even move back into room 52.)

Throughout the night, awful noises come from different rooms as they become too dangerous to sleep in. EVERY TIME this happens, you move through one door to any of the neighboring rooms. You are allowed to go back to a room you've been in before, providing it is still safe.

If you survive until the morning, go to the page indicated by the room number you finish in. If something goes wrong with the room you are in, go straight to that page number.

The question is, can you survive the night?

You started in room 52, then the noise of room 139 collapsing made you move. When room 70 became snake-infested, you moved again.

VALOOSH! A raging river full of piranha fish breaks through into room 28. You move again.

WHIFF! A two-hundred-year-old cheese-and-pickle sandwich suddenly gasses out room 54. Time to move.

KARUNCH! A runaway steamroller flattens room 12. I hope you weren't in there! Move again.

DOY-YOY-YOING! A bungee-jumping elephant lands in room 6. If you haven't been turned into a pancake, keep moving!

GROAN! Somebody who has just decoded *The Deadliest Joke in the Universe* (another ace book) has arrived in room 10 and wants a victim to try it out on. This is probably the most dangerous room of all! Out of here!

KUR-REAK! The floor suddenly rots away in room 26, revealing a lake of boiling poison underneath. You move again.

CLANK, DONK, RUMBLE, ZOCK! A clockwork suit of armor suddenly runs riot with an ax in room 86. Quick, get going.

SPLURGE! A bowl of petunias turns out to be a giant meat-eating Gobble Shrub in room 52. That's where you started, so I hope you didn't go back for anything. Keep moving.

BUZZZ! Well, guess what? Six thousand ghastly gnats have swarmed out of the sink drain hole in room 88. Move again.

FLIPPETY-SPLOP! A forgotten bag of old socks has mutated into a slime monster in room 14. Quick, move again.

ZAP, FIZZ, CRACKLE! What's the chance of being hit by lightning? It's 100 percent if you're in room 38. Move if you can. If not, then bye-bye.

SPLUTTLE, SPLITHER! Gross! Ye olde Slimey Snayles and Slugges have slimed into room 32 and taken it over.

TUR-RING! What's that? Thank goodness, it's your alarm clock telling you that morning has arrived. But are you still around to hear it? If so, it's time to check out of the Ghastly Guest House!

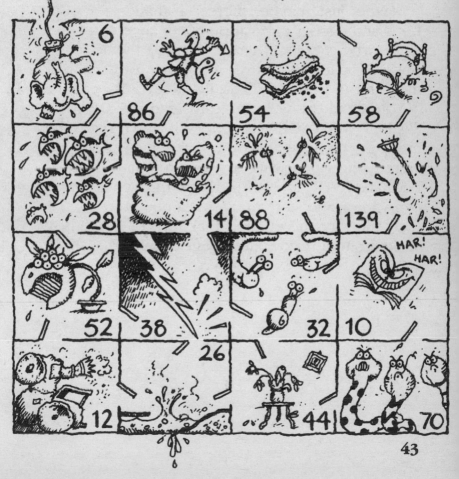

Have you still got some empty boxes left on the very last page? Well, now's the time to put a letter S in each one. (Of course, if you've got millions of empty boxes, then even YOU might realize you've done something a bit wrong!)

Can you read the message? No? Then DO YOU WANT TO GIVE UP? Have the Killer Puzzles finally beaten you?

Maybe, just maybe, there's a chance for you. Look at the letter in position 65. Change that letter to O wherever it appears. Change the letter in position 54 to E wherever it appears. Now change the letter in position 68 to T wherever it appears.

You should now be able to read the DEADLY SECRET MESSAGE! (If you still can't read the message, then what can I say? I just hope you were using a pencil when you wrote in this book, because you'll have to go back through it, erase everything, and start all over again!)

By the way, the number that appears in the box at the bottom is your next page number.

Mushrooms

You decide to make some extra money by picking wild mushrooms and selling them. The trouble is, some of the mushrooms aren't mushrooms! They are FIENDISH FUNGUS and FATAL to FEED ON.

Any mushroom with a tall pointy top is definitely safe unless the stalk matches the top or the stalk is plain, in which case it might not be safe.

Any mushroom with a striped-stalk is definitely FATAL if it has a flat top.

Any mushroom with a polka dot stalk is definitely safe unless it has a striped top, in which case it might be FATAL.

Any mushroom with a plain stalk will definitely be safe if the top has polka dots.

Can you work out which mushrooms are DEFINITELY safe?
If you sell each one for 10 cents, how much money will you make? Turn to that page.

By the way, if you still have a glass of water next to you, you can drink it up and relax. If you haven't got a glass of water AND your pants are dry, then you're going to have a very miserable time trying to finish this book.

Good grief! What are you doing here? It should be impossible for you to find this page because

This is the Phantom Page 113!

Look at the number on each of these two pages. They're both 113, aren't they? In fact, look at the previous page – it's 47. And the next page is 48 (and still warm from your last mental exertions). This page is . . . NOT HERE.

Well, now that you *are* here, let's give you a puzzle to do.

This is THE PHANTOM LOST PROPERTY OFFICE.

Six phantoms have called in to collect missing items. Unfortunately, the manager, Eygore, has lent his brain out for an experiment, so he can't exactly remember which box holds which item.

The box containing Julius Caesar's dagger has a lower number than the one with the Lone Ranger's mask.

Dracula's false teeth are on the left-hand side, next to a box containing some metal.

Lady MacBeth's theater ticket is on the bottom row. It is not next to the dagger.

Jacob Marley's chains are on the top row.

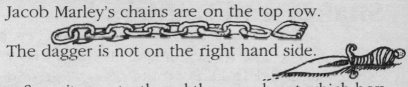

The dagger is not on the right hand side.

So, grit your teeth and then work out which box contains ANNE BOLEYN'S HEAD. Go to the page number on that box.

82 84 70

68 26 12

Brain   Eygore

Snakes and Ladders

Here's a neat little game for you. Do you know how Snakes and Ladders works? Easy. You start on the start square (surprise, surprise) and throw one dice. You then move as many squares as the dice says. If you finish your move on the bottom of a ladder, you go up to the top. If you finish on the top of a snake, you slide down to the bottom.

Pretend you have a normal dice and you roll it SIX times, and every time you get a different number. Write down the letters of the squares you finish each turn on, and they will spell out a message. Of course, the message might be some rubbish like TU-VEN-EPA-EIG-EPA-RE (that's what rolling the sequence 3, 2, 6, 5, 4, 1 would give you). But if you roll the six different numbers in the right order, you will find out where to go next!

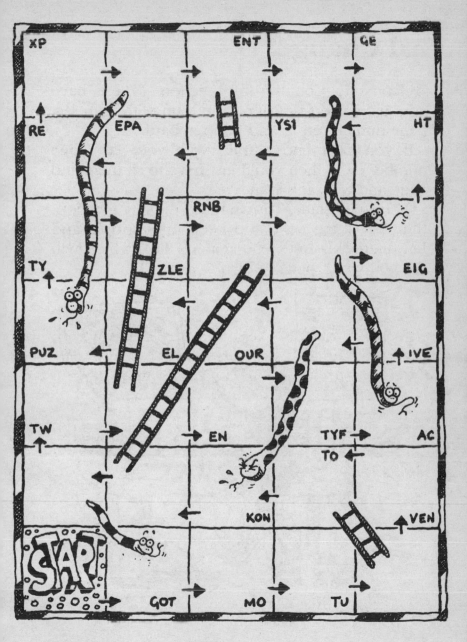

49

All Change!

Welcome to Conundrum Junction. Where have you just come from? Find the train with your last page number on it, and jump aboard.

If you can't find a train with your last page number on it, then you'll just have to sit there and wait, and wait, and wait. . . .

Your train starts. Turn right at the first junction, then left at the next, and keep turning right and left alternately until you reach a flag, which will tell you which page to turn to next.

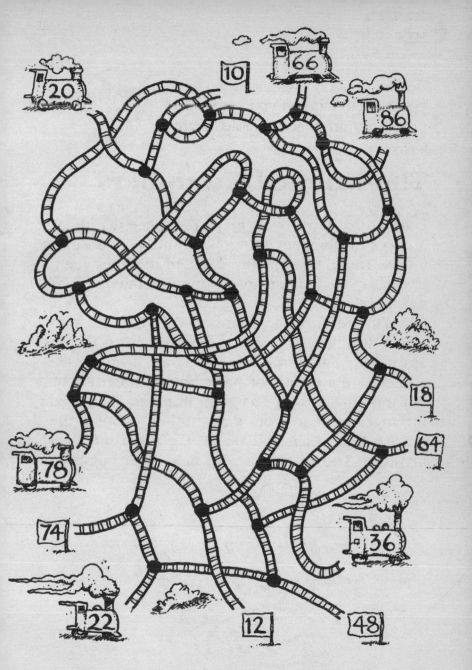

Before you do any more puzzles, you have to take off your socks and put them into some cold water. Go on!

The Knotted Knumbers

Look at that mess over there! You'll see that there are lots of numbers written out and jammed into a box. There are so many of them that they have to overlap each other. Overlapping numbers make a "number knot."

You'll see that the number ELEVEN has two eights attached to it, and a line has been drawn around this number knot to separate it off.

There are a couple of other little number knots, but the biggest knot has eight numbers all linked up together. Can you draw a line around the biggest knot, then add up all the eight numbers involved? The answer is your next page number.

E	I	G	H	T	S	T	Y
L	F	I	F	T	E	E	N
E	I	G	H	T	V	E	O
V	X	O	T	F	E	N	U
E	T	T	W	E	N	T	Y
N	Y	F	O	U	R	N	T
T	H	I	R	T	Y	I	W
T	E	V	O	H	O	N	E
E	S	E	N	R	U	I	L
N	I	N	E	E	R	N	V
E	X	E	N	E	R	E	E

Ms. Tayk, the Terrible Typist

If you've ever seen a typewriter or a computer keyboard, you know that the letters and numbers are set out like this:

```
1 2 3 4 5 6 7 8 9 0
 Q W E R T Y U I O P
  A S D F G H J K L
   Z X C V B N M
```

Ms. Tayk is the world's worst typist because . . . she's in love with Bony Tony. She spends all day dreaming about him, and she even types him love letters. Here's how one of them starts:

F3qf 5pb7

Can you read that? Of course not. You see, she's so silly that every time she tries to hit a letter, she misses and gets one of the letters on the keyboard above, below, or next to it instead. For instance, if she wanted to type the letter R, she might hit E, D, F, T, or even 4 or 5.

If you look carefully you'll see her letter is supposed to start, "Dear Tony," but instead of hitting the letter D she hit F, instead of e she hit 3, and so on.

Here's the rest of the letter:

K pibw tp7 jqsk6 qbf J
I love you madly and I

2zm5 69 m9zz 798 pm 7p74
want

p9c3k6 4sx k8oz

You'll see the first line has been decoded for you, but it got too yuckily disgusting, so the rest is up to you if you're the sort of person who likes reading other people's silly letters.

Now, here's the BAD NEWS! She's written another message that you'll have to decode. You'll just have to hope it isn't a love letter to YOU.

Bp 59 oqb4 z9z67 62p

Misery Nick

Down in Dastardly Dungeons, the old jailer, Misery
Nick, is checking on his inmates.

How many prisoners does Misery Nick have?
That's your next page number.

59

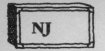
The Teeth Sharpener

Gnora Gnash wanted to get her teeth sharpened, so she phoned the dentist for directions to his office. However, the dentist is a bit frightened of Gnora's monstrous molars, so he tried to confuse her. He didn't dare to actually lie to her, but this is what he did say:

"When you leave your house, drive along the road until you go under a bridge. Take the first right turn and then take the second turn off the traffic circle. Keep going until you've been OVER a bridge, then take your first right turn and then the next left. Follow the road until you've been OVER two more bridges, then take the first left. Take the fourth turn off the traffic circle, then take the first turn, then take the first right turn. Keep going, and the office is right in front of you."

Which house is Gnora setting off from? Go to that page.

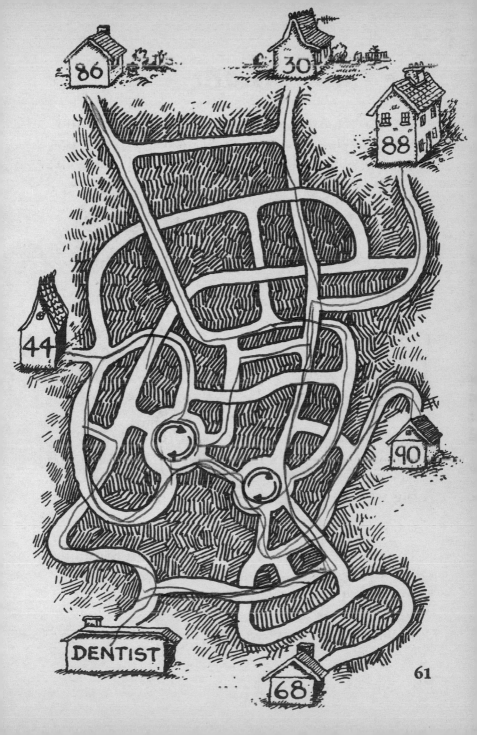

86

30

88

44

90

DENTIST

68

61

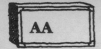

The Clown Outfit

You discover Auntie Myrtle is coming to tea, and to avoid having your face splattered by a massive, sloppy, lipsticky kiss, you think of a brilliant plan . . . you disguise yourself as a clown.

Before you start this puzzle, you need to have a glass of water next to you, so go and get one. Go on. OK, as long as you've got your water ready, we can continue.

To be a clown, you need twelve items, as follows:

Two gloves
An orange wig
Baggy trousers
Two shoes
Two socks
A striped t-shirt
A bowler hat
A jacket
A big squirty flower

The trouble is, the clown costume firm is run by clowns. They only sell clown costumes in boxes, with three items in each box.

Which boxes do you need to buy to get a complete clown outfit as cheaply as possible?

When you've worked out the cheapest price in dollars, turn to that page number.

By the way, clown shoes and gloves don't have a left or right, they fit on either side.

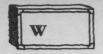

Outer Space!

Flying above you are thirteen space stations, and they are linked up using space-warp beams. You can travel along the beams between the different stations. Your challenge is that you have to set off from the space base, visit every station ONCE (no more), and then finish up back at the base again.

What is the number of the SEVENTH station you visit? Turn to that page.

The Doubtful Derby

Look at these four racehorses, Nutter, Alien, Pegasus, and Beast. They all look a bit shaky, don't you think?

Each jockey's shirt is a different color. The red shirt doesn't have polka dots, but the blue one does. The jockey riding Nutter doesn't have the gold shirt (and, incidentally, the jockey with the green shirt won the prettiest jockey competition). The jockey on Pegasus has the blue shirt.

Alien came in second in the race. His jockey has a polka-dot shirt. The gold shirt finished third. Beast finished the race sometime after the jockey with the plain shirt.

What number is the horse that won?

(Here's a hint: first work out what color Alien's shirt is, then Nutter's, then Beast's. After that you should be able to work out the winner.)

The Cheating Page

This page is here to help out people who are not mega-brainy.

If you ARE mega-brainy, then you can go straight to page 30. Bye-bye.

BUT, if you do need some hints, first of all you must get a BOX OF CORNFLAKES! Now read on . . .

Luckily for you, we've managed to sneak some hints out of the offices of the KILLER PUZZLES INTERNATIONAL CORPORATION. Unfortunately, they're a bit mixed up, but if you've been stuck on a puzzle or are not sure about an answer, look here and you might find a clue to help you. The trouble is, this information doesn't come free.

Before you read the hints, YOU MUST PUT A HANDFUL OF CORNFLAKES DOWN YOUR SHIRT! Go on, a nice big handful.

The Moldy Milkshakes are off and the picture starts crooked but the cat straightens it. Bertie has a bow tie, Fingers tells the truth, and there is one fish under each striped lily pad. Your first three throws should be 3, then 5 to go up a ladder, then 1 to come down a snake, and Fish Tails are off, too. One Poke is about $4.29, the mask is directly above the ticket, and you shouldn't be selling any mushrooms with checkered parts. Bill has the smallest appetite, and the calculator answer is 811 less than it was.

The Worm Pages

In fact, these worms are bookworms. Can you hear a faint chewing noise? That's the sound of the worms eating through the pages. If you can't hear it, put your head next to the book . . . BUT NOT TOO CLOSE! The worms might jump into your ear and eat their way through your brain until they come out of your nose!

The worms move through the book by eating their way from page to page. So if

---

Now then, have a look at these six worms.

One of these worms can only eat through one page, one worm can eat two, one can eat three, one can eat four, one can eat five, and the piggiest worm can eat through six pages. Simon eats twice as many pages as Dave, and incidentally, both Dave and Simon have lots of hair. Fred, who hasn't got any stripes, eats four more pages than

BE CAREFUL! You might find you arrive on this page more than once! The SECOND time you arrive here, find out where SIMON goes and continue from there. The THIRD time you arrive here, find out where BERTIE goes and continue from there. The FOURTH time, go and get a stamp and stick it on your nose and leave it there for a week. . . .

If this worm ate through three pages, he would come out between pages 76 and 77.

Bill. Neither Dave nor Bertie have hats on. Bertie eats two pages less than Henry. Bill and Simon both wear shades.

You have to work out who Henry is and find out which page he will end up on, then you have to go and solve the puzzle on that page.

How are you doing? Feeling confident? Do you think you've got everything right so far? Good for you!

OK, just to make things even more fun, we'll try and confuse you. Go and find the biggest pair of pants in your house. If they are pink and frilly, that's even better. When you've got them, hold them tightly in your hand until you're told otherwise. Ready? Set? Go!

The Icing Beetle

Look at this big cake! It's been cut into lots of square pieces, and they're all covered in icing.

The trouble is, there's an Icing Beetle about, which eats icing! Every time it walks across a piece of cake, it eats all the icing on it.

The beetle gradually works his way over the cake, eating the icing as he goes. He moves:

Up two pieces, right two, up two, left two, down one, left one, up two, right one, up four, right three, down one, right one, down three, right two, up two, left one, up one, right two, down four, left one, down two, left two, up two.

Can you mark out his path by shading in the icing he eats? Look in the central square for your next page number.

Smelly Green Slime

Oh, yuck! This pond is full of smelly green slime.

All you have to do is find out how many fish there are in the pond. Hold your nose, stick your head under the surface, and start counting. . . .

Luckily, there is another way of finding out. The fish are all hiding under the lily pads. Each lily pad might be hiding one or two fish, or maybe none at all. Every lily pad has a frog sitting on it. The frog can't see under its own lily pad, but it can see all the fish under the lily pads touching its own. The number on the frogs' backs shows how many fish they can see.

Here's a little example of some lily pads, the frogs on them, and how many fish are under each (marked in the little box):

Can you work out how many fish are under each lily pad? Remember, it can only be 0, 1, or 2. When you've finished, add them all up and go to that page number. A few numbers have already been put in to help you.

Cleopatra's Crossword

Lucky you, because now we're going to Egypt. It's a great place to explore, and right now I sphinx we'll disa-pyramid the ruins for a Pharaoh-ld time looking in an ancient tomb. . . .

The experts have spent many years studying the hieroglyphics, but we're going to have a look at the lowero-glyphics, because among them is one of the oldest Killer Puzzles of all time: Cleopatra's Crossword.

You'll see the crossword grid has room for seven five-letter words. Each word goes in a straight line, and the arrows show you how they fit in. Here's one of the crossword clues:

ＴＵＵ ＡＤ ＴＹＤＴＡＤＹ?

Simple, eh? No? You mean you can't read it? Oh, well, in that case I suppose we'll have to give you the answers, and you can just fit them in the grid. (Some of them might have to go in backward, by the way.)

Now it's simple, isn't it? All you have to do is see which letter appears in the bottom space, and then turn to the page number that corresponds to that symbol.

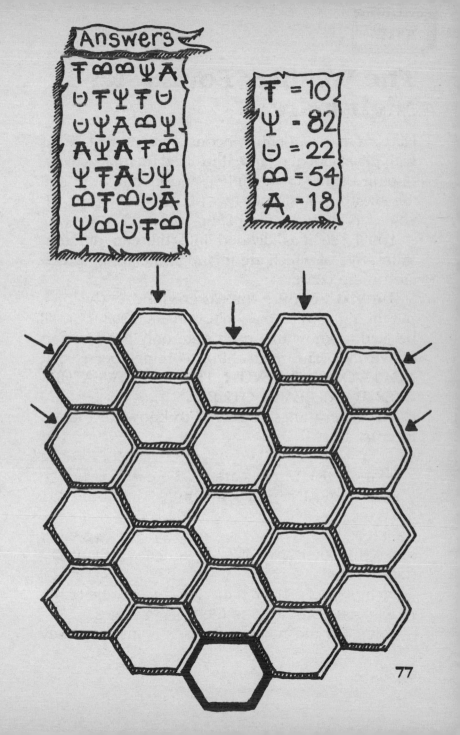

The Weather Forecaster's Nightmare

Here's a map of a rather inconstant continent. What with gravitational relapse, localized thermal activity, photon beams from Jupiter, and global warming, the weather is simply too bizarre for words. (If you're trying to plan a picnic, forget it.)

You'll see it is divided into thirteen different states, five of which are inland and eight of which are on the coast.

Can you help the forecaster, Anne T. Cyclone, put the right weather symbol on each state? You'll be glad to know that each state only has one sort of weather. The main thing to remember is that NO TWO STATES WITH THE SAME WEATHER EVER TOUCH EACH OTHER.

The other things you need to know for today's forecast are:

Both CLOUDY states are on the east coast.

Both the RAINY states touch the river but NOT the coast.

One of the SNOWY states only touches two other states, the other SNOWY state touches a CLOUDY state.

Each of the FOGGY states is between one of the RAINY states and one of the SUNNY states.

Neither of the WINDY states is inland, but they

both touch a CLOUDY state.

Which state has the THUNDERSTORM? When you've found its number, turn to that page.

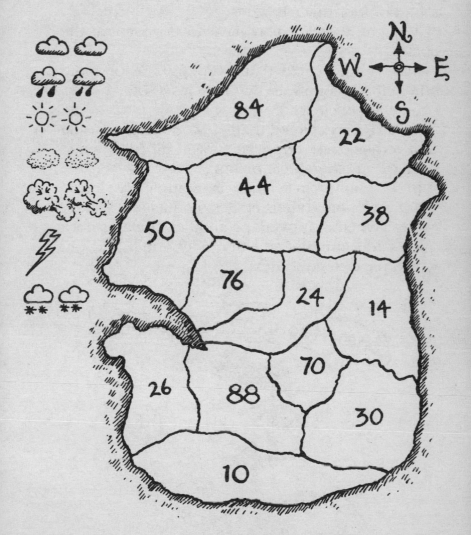

Come on! Too easy, you think. Counting's too easy for a book of Killer Puzzles.

All right, then, all you have to do is count the circles.

BUT . . . any circle that overlaps one or more other circles counts as TWO circles. (So
counts as six circles.)

AND . . . any circle that is completely inside ONE other circle doesn't count at all (whether it overlaps another circle or not).

BUT . . . any circle that is completely inside TWO or more other circles counts as THREE circles (whether it overlaps another circle or not).

So start counting, and that way you'll find out which page to go to next!

Ha! You have been got by the CURSE OF THE MUMMY'S TOMB! When you're asleep tonight you will be infested by the plague of the seventy scarabs. The only way to avoid your body being beetled to a beastly, blotchy blob is to spend the rest of the day walking like an Egyptian.

You have to stand like this:

and walk sideways. If you do that, the scarabs *might* leave you alone.

If you make it through the night, then tomorrow you can stop being Egyptian and go back to whichever puzzle you came from and try again.

If you're having trouble with a certain crossword, here's a clue: you'll see three of the words have the same middle letter. If you think about it, you'll realize that letter has to go in the middle space of the crossword.

As for the pyramid bricks, the real ones have just two spotted sides, which are next to each other.

Welcome to the

Congratulations Page!

Congratulations on reaching page 83! You're really making progress. Are you remembering to fill the letters into the grid at the end of the book? Of course you are, because you're so SMART.

Now then, Big Brains, here's a special secret message:

NQIASG AWYROT DENAR KCNABJ OGRA HTAHT AHSGNSO RIWEWLZIZ UOPTLSAEL EAHTS TOPGUF OYYYLYL ACUTACA

(As you're so stunningly cunning, you'll have realized that all you have to do is read it backward. Oh, and obviously you have to miss out every third letter.)

The Odd Page

IMPORTANT NOTICE: You'll be glad to know it's safe to breathe again.

Good grief! Look over there.

This book has been invaded by a page from another book. Bah! We can't have that. Prepare to cross it out, burn it, eat it with ketchup. . . .

Wait! Did you know that sometimes books can contain SECRET MESSAGES? Sometimes you get a message if you miss out every second word. Sometimes you miss out one word, then miss out two words alternately. Other times there's a message if you just read every third or every fourth or even every fifth word. Sometimes you have to take the second letter of every word then write them all out backward and translate them into Swedish. In fact, sometimes you have to sing the words to *Three Blind Mice* while having hiccups in an elevator.

"Go quickly my darling and when you arrive do kiss Henry."

However, the Duchess could not puzzle it out. "What on earth for?" gasped the astonished woman.

"His page delivered this message before afternoon tea," muttered the Duke. "It says, 'One simply cannot bear you not being here'."

Just then an arrow came through the window from the greenhouse.

The Parachutist

This is more of a challenge than a puzzle. You have to lay this book open on the floor, then drop a small coin or a baked bean or a paper wad on to this page. When your "parachutist" lands on an island, you have to follow the instructions.

By the way, have you recently taken your socks off? If you have, you'll have to PUT THEM BACK ON if you land in the sea.

Rush off to Page 50

Go and Kiss the Fridge

So, you've got to page 88, eh? As a reward, here's a special game for you to play:

Go and borrow a lipstick, then stand in front of a mirror. Copy this pattern on to your forehead:

Now grab your teddy bear and have a good cry. Sorry, but you've been defeated by the Killer Puzzles.

Are you going to have another go? If so, then turn to page 3. Yes, page 3, right back to the start. It's your only hope.

Maybe you're too feeble to want to start again? In that case, here are some other things you could do with this book:

Wear it on your head and pretend it's a fabulous new hat.

Put it under the leg of a chair and then sit down and have a good wobble.

Use it as a handkerchief next time you want to sneeze.

Fold it in half, then fold it in half again so it's a quarter of the size, then fold it once more to make it really tiny. (If you can do that then you don't need to be brainy.)

Have a bath, and then use it as a towel.

Cover it with gravy and serve it with potatoes, zucchinis, and minted carrots.

But of course, the BEST idea is to pass this book to someone else, and see if they can do it! Before you do, dry your teddy bear out. Your friend might need to borrow it next!

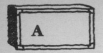
Freaky Fred's Fashion Show!

It's a dirty, nasty business, the fashion world. As soon as somebody invents a super new look, somebody else tries to steal it.

Freaky Fred has revealed his spring collection. Here it is:

Fred has also designed a new outfit, but already people have copied it. Here come the supermodels on the catwalk. Only one of them is wearing the real Freaky Fred outfit. All the others have one detail wrong.

Which number is Fred's? That's your next page number.

The Cowfield

There's some good news and some bad news. The good news is that there are no cows in the field. (They've been mooved.) The bad news is that they have left behind some KILLER COWPATS! Ukky pooh.

Hold your nose, you're going in. You must start from the top and move in the direction of the arrow. You must move in straight lines (up, down, left or right), and you can only change direction when you reach a stone. Your challenge is to leave the field by one of the other gates. Of course, if you step in a cowpat you've got to stay here! Nobody wants you tramping through the book with you-know-what all over your feet.

If you get out with clean feet, turn to whichever page the gate tells you to.

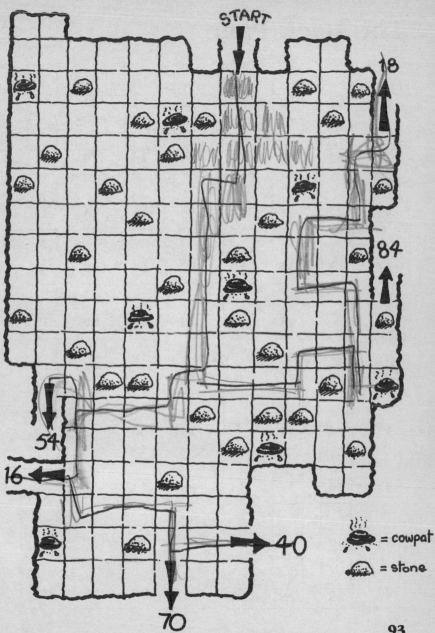

START

18

84

54

16

40

70

= cowpat

= stone

The Back Page

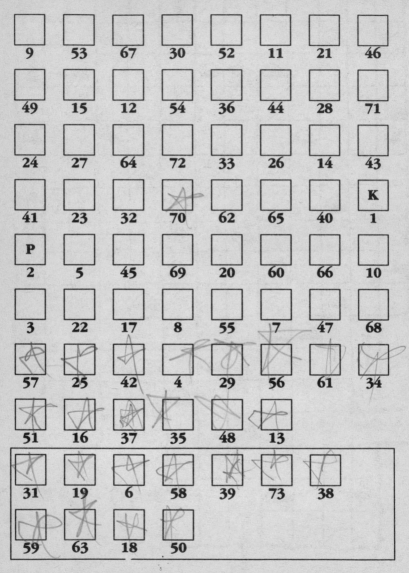

9	53	67	30	52	11	21	46
49	15	12	54	36	44	28	71
24	27	64	72	33	26	14	43
41	23	32	70	62	65	40	K 1
P 2	5	45	69	20	60	66	10
3	22	17	8	55	7	47	68
57	25	42	4	29	56	61	34
51	16	37	35	48	13		

31	19	6	58	39	73	38
59	63	18	50			

DO NOT WRITE ANYTHING ON THIS PAGE.

TURN OVER FOR THE VERY LAST PAGE.

The Very Back Page!

48	67	27	69	12	44	72	26
5	73	68	**P** 2	63	22	11	40
66	34	64	35	13	23	45	62
33	53	**K** 1	14	54	28	9	10
47	17	15	55	29	70	46	56
18	16	41	3	19	20	39	57
31	8	30	21	49	4	58	25
32	7	59	50	71	60	37	51	43
36	65	6	52	24	38	61	42